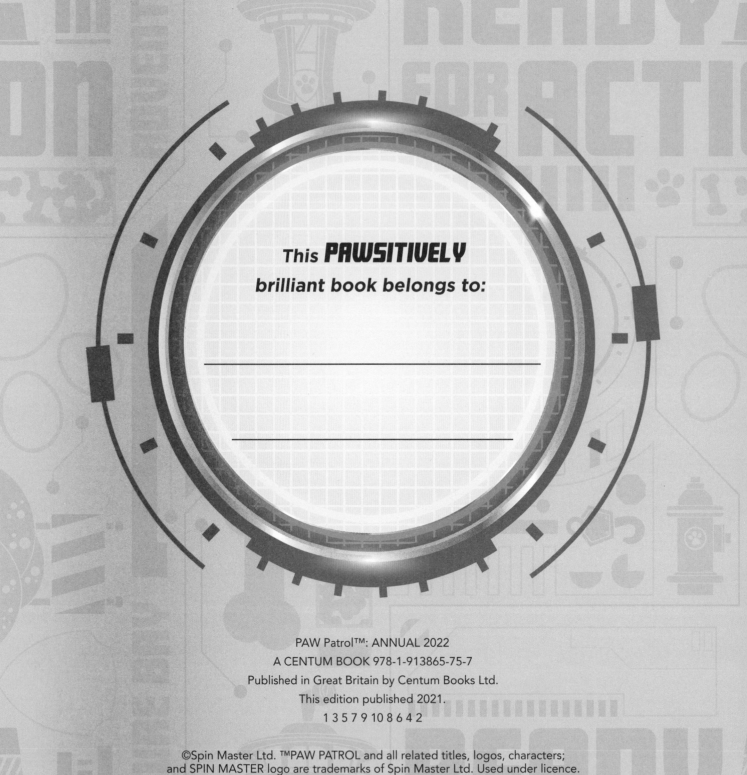

This **PAWSITIVELY**
brilliant book belongs to:

_____

_____

PAW Patrol™: ANNUAL 2022
A CENTUM BOOK 978-1-913865-75-7
Published in Great Britain by Centum Books Ltd.
This edition published 2021.
1 3 5 7 9 10 8 6 4 2

books@centumbooksltd.co.uk

CENTUM BOOKS LIMITED. Reg. No. 07641486

A CIP catalogue record for this book is available from
the British Library.

Printed in China.

ANNUAL 2022

Centum

CONTENTS

Calling all PAW Patrol Fans! It's time for some PAWsome activity fun!

This book is packed with pup-tastic puzzles, challenges and missions to complete, plus profiles of all your favourite pup pals and a fun story to share. So what are you waiting for? **Let's roll with the PAW Patrol!**

TRACK A TREAT!

There are 10 very special pup treats hidden on the pages throughout this book. **Colour in a treat each time you find one.**

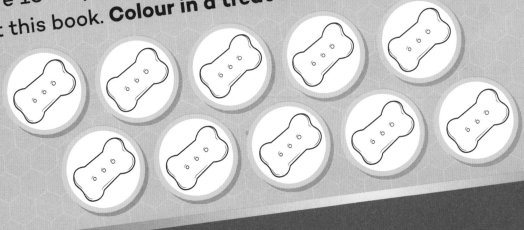

TO THE LOOKOUT!

There's an emergency in Adventure Bay! Ryder is calling the PAW Patrol to the Lookout, but his PupPad has gone wrong! It's mixed up all the pups' names! Can you help him unscramble them all?

A YKCOR

B LEBBUR

C MRSAAHLL

D HEASC

E YKSE

F MAZU

Write the correct name under each pup.

REPORTING FOR DUTY!

Ryder needs ALL the pups for the rescue mission, but someone is still missing. Who is it?

Tick off the pups as you spot them in the picture, then fill in the name of the missing pup.

The missing pup is:

_____

PROFILE: MARSHALL

He's all fired up!

NAME: Marshall

BREED: Dalmatian

ROLE: Fire pup and Medic pup

UNIFORM COLOUR: Red

GADGETS:
Pup Pack with a
double-spray fire hose

VEHICLE: Fire engine

SKILLS: Putting out
fires, rescuing animals,
medical help

CATCHPHRASE:

READY FOR A RUFF-RUFF RESCUE!

DID YOU KNOW?

Marshall's medical supplies include an X-ray screen to check pups and people for injuries!

10

MYSTERY MESSAGE

Ryder has sent a coded message to Marshall.
Circle every other letter to find out what it says.
The first letter has been circled to start you off.

Write the message here:

__F__ __I__ __R__ __E__ ! / __C__ __O__ __M__ __E__ / __Q__ __U__ __I__ __C__ __K__ !

11

HAT MATCH!

Each pup has a special uniform and hat to wear on rescue missions. Draw lines to match each pup with their hat.

Circle the pup with no hat and draw it for them here.

CHASE IS ON THE CASE!

Help Chase to reach the Lookout in super-quick time. Choose the path with the fewest cones blocking his way!

ANSWER ON PAGE 44

13

PROFILE: CHASE

NAME: Chase

BREED: German Shepherd

ROLE: Police pup and Spy pup

UNIFORM COLOUR: Blue

GADGETS: Pup Pack with megaphone, searchlight and a net that can shoot out to catch things

VEHICLE: Police truck

SKILLS: Directing traffic, blocking dangers, solving mysteries

CATCHPHRASE:

CHASE IS ON THE CASE!

DID YOU KNOW?

Chase can sniff out anything – but he's allergic to cats and feathers!

SPOT THE DIFFERENCE

Chase is an expert at catching things with his net! **Can you spot 5 differences** between these two pictures of the police pup in action?

Colour in a star each time you find a difference.

ANSWERS ON **PAGE 44**

15

TRUCK TROUBLE!

Trace along the paths without touching the sides to help the pups reach their vehicles, so they can zoom to the rescue.

If you touch the sides, try again using a different coloured pen.

PUP TO PUP!

Draw lines to match the pup pairs. Which pup does not have a match?

Write the pup's name here:

FRIENDS FOREVER!

The PAW Patrol have lots of friends in Adventure Bay. How many of them can you find in the grid below? Tick each name as you spot it in the grid. If you can't find someone, put a cross next to their name.

F	T	I	C	A	L	I	O	S	C
A	H	V	H	S	J	A	K	E	A
R	M	R	P	O	R	T	E	R	P
M	J	G	C	R	S	A	Y	B	N
E	W	A	L	L	Y	G	I	E	T
R	G	V	I	K	O	P	A	T	U
Y	A	H	C	A	E	K	G	T	R
U	D	W	H	T	P	R	U	I	B
M	N	H	V	I	D	Q	X	N	O
I	W	A	L	E	X	O	N	A	T

○ KATIE

○ FARMER YUMI

○ CAP'N TURBOT

○ MAYOR GOODWAY

○ BETTINA

○ ALEX

○ JAKE

○ CALI

○ WALLY

○ CHICKALETTA

○ WALLY

CLUE!
There are two names missing from the grid!

TIME FOR A TREAT!

Draw lines to match each pup with their food bowl.
Then test out your spotting skills by answering the questions.

1. Which pup has the most treats? _____

2. Which pup has a green bowl? _____

3. Which pup's bowl contains only yellow treats? _____

4. Who has the most red treats? _____

ANSWERS ON PAGE 44

PROFILE: RUBBLE

Let's dig it!

NAME: Rubble

BREED: Bulldog

ROLE: Construction pup

UNIFORM COLOUR: Yellow

GADGETS: Pup Pack with a bucket arm scoop

VEHICLE: Digger with a bucket shovel and drill

SKILLS: Building, digging, lifting and transporting heavy things

CATCHPHRASE:

HERE COMES RUBBLE ON THE DOUBLE!

DID YOU KNOW?

Rubble loves to get covered in mud and then visit Katie's Pet Parlour for a warm bubble bath!

DOTTY ABOUT DIGGING

Rubble just loves to dig! **Join the dots** to complete his bucket scoop arm, so he can get to work right away.

Now colour in your picture of the construction pup.

TO THE RESCUE

Pick the items you would choose for these pup-tastic challenges.

1 Ryder needs to get a message to the pups quickly. **What would work best?**

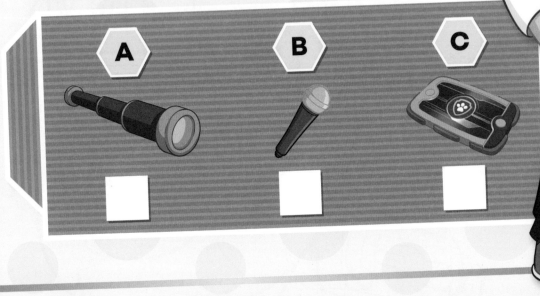

A

B

C

2 Rocky needs to fix some dangerously loose nails in a go-kart. **What does he need from his pack?**

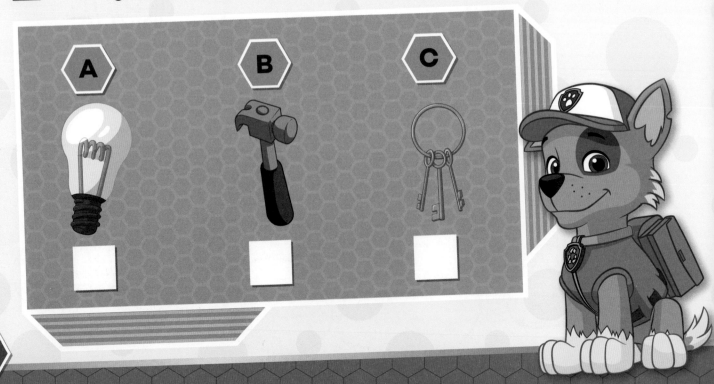

A

B

C

3 Help! The pups have an emergency in deep snow.
Which vehicle can get there?

A ☐

B ☐   C ☐

4 Cali is stuck in a tall tree and only Marshall can help.
What item should he use?

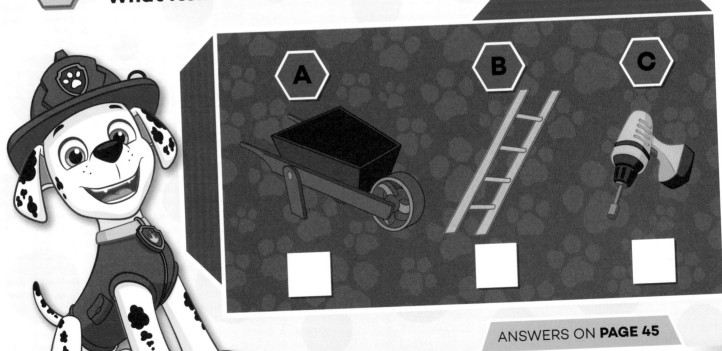

A   B   C

☐   ☐   ☐

ANSWERS ON **PAGE 45**

PROFILE: SKYE

NAME: Skye

BREED: Cockapoo

ROLE: Pilot pup

UNIFORM COLOUR: Pink

GADGETS: Pup Pack with wings that allow her to take flight

VEHICLE: Helicopter

SKILLS: Flying, flips and spins!

CATCHPHRASE:

THIS PUP'S GOTTA FLY!

DID YOU KNOW?

Skye is really brave and very little frightens her, but one thing she is afraid of is eagles.

SKY HIGH

Alex's kite has blown away on the breeze. Help Skye find her way through the clouds to rescue it.

How many birds does Skye meet on her way?

ANSWERS ON **PAGE 45**

ON THE FARM

The pups are helping Farmer Yumi as she prepares Mr Porter's weekly delivery. **Can you answer the questions about the scene?**

1	How many **LAMBS** are in the picture?
2	Which **DIGGER PUP** is missing?
3	How many **CARROTS** can you count?
4	There is a pile of another type of **VEGETABLE** – what is it?
5	What kind of **BUG** can you spot in the picture?

Can you spot these pictures in the scene? **Tick them when you find them.**

ANSWERS ON **PAGE 45**

PROFILE: ZUMA

Let's dive in!

NAME: Zuma

BREED: Labrador

ROLE: Water-rescue pup

UNIFORM COLOUR: Orange

GADGETS: Pup Pack with air tanks and propellers for diving and swimming underwater

VEHICLE: Hovercraft that can travel on land or water

SKILLS: Rescuing sea animals, underwater missions, water sports

CATCHPHRASE:

READY, SET, GET WET!

DID YOU KNOW?

Zuma's hovercraft can transform into a **submarine** for deep underwater adventures!

FISHY FRIENDS

Follow the instructions below to colour in Zuma's fishy friends and make a PAWsome underwater scene.

Colour **4** fish red.
Colour **3** fish yellow.
Colour **2** fish blue.
Colour **2** fish orange.
Colour **1** fish pink.

How many fish are there altogether?

_____

29

ANSWERS ON **PAGE 45**

ADVENTURE BAY HANGOUT

Where would you most love to visit in Adventure Bay? **Try this game to find out.**

Choose a toy.
1
a. Yoyo
b. Teddy bear
c. Skateboard
d. Kite

Pick an animal.
2
a. Horse
b. Penguin
c. Rabbit
d. Seal

Circle your favourite season.
3
a. Spring
b. Winter
c. Autumn
d. Summer

4 **Pick your favourite pup.**
a. Marshall
b. Everest
c. Rubble
d. Zuma

5 **Choose a colour.**
a. Green
b. Purple
c. Pink
d. Yellow

Now count up your answers to find your hangout!

Mostly As

Farmer Yumi's Farm

Mostly Bs

Jake's Mountain

Mostly Cs

Katie's Pet Parlour

Mostly Ds

Adventure Bay Beach

PROFILE: ROCKY

Rocky to the rescue!

NAME: Rocky

BREED: Mixed breed

ROLE: Recycling pup

UNIFORM COLOUR: Green

GADGETS: Pup Pack with a mechanical claw and lots of handy tools

VEHICLE: Recycling truck

SKILLS: Creativity and ideas, fixing things, solving problems

CATCHPHRASE:

DON'T LOSE IT – REUSE IT!

DID YOU KNOW?

Rocky doesn't like getting wet at all, which means bath time isn't much fun!

TIDY UP TIME!

Rocky needs to sort out the rubbish for recycling. Can you help him by drawing lines to match up the items that are the same?

PROFILE: EVEREST

Born to slide!

NAME: Everest

BREED: Husky

ROLE: Mountain-rescue pup

UNIFORM COLOUR:
Turquoise and yellow

GADGETS: Pup Pack with a grappling hook and foldable, rocket-powered snowboard

VEHICLE: Snowcat with a claw to grab large objects, and transport a sledge

SKILLS: Snowy rescues, climbing icy slopes, super-fast snowboarding

CATCHPHRASE:

ICE OR SNOW, I'M READY TO GO!

DID YOU KNOW?

Everest likes **belly-bogganing**, where she slides down the slopes on her belly!

DOT TO DOT

Everest is on her way to play with the penguins. **Join the dots** to complete her snowcat, then draw three penguins and colour in your picture.

RUFF-RUFF COUNTING!

Help the pups to complete the tasks by drawing the correct number of things in each box.

Chase puts out **7** road cones.

Rocky places **4** plastic bottles in the bin.

Rubble finds a hammer and **10** nails.

Everest makes **6** snowballs.

PROFILE: TRACKER

Buenos dias, PAW Patrol!

NAME: Tracker

BREED: Chihuahua

ROLE: Jungle-rescue pup

UNIFORM COLOUR: Green

GADGETS: Pup Pack with a compass, torch and grappling cables

VEHICLE: Jeep with a special radar tracking system

SKILLS: Jungle rescues, super-hearing (thanks to his big ears!)

CATCHPHRASE:
I'M ALL EARS!

DID YOU KNOW?

Tracker can speak two languages – English and Spanish.

TRACKER TIME

Tracker is on the trail of someone special.
**Can you help the jungle pup sniff his way through
the maze to find him?** Then answer the questions.

How many skunks did Tracker meet on the way?

Who did Tracker find?

What other creature is hiding in the jungle?

ANSWERS ON **PAGE 45**

PAMPERED POOCH

Rubble is visiting Katie's Pet Parlour for some pampering!
Can you spot eight differences between these two pictures?
Colour in a paw print for every difference you spot.

ANSWERS ON **PAGE 45**

BEST PUP EVER!

Who's your favourite member of the PAW Patrol? **Draw a present for the lucky pup here** to say thank you for being such a pup-tastic hero. Don't forget to write their name on the label!

How about something yummy to eat, a new toy or an exciting storybook?

Dear..............................

Thank you for being so **PAWSOME!**

UP CLOSE

Look carefully at these close ups. **Can you work out who they are?** Write the names underneath the pictures.

WORD PLAY

How many new words can you make using the letters in this phrase?

PAW PATROL, READY FOR ACTION!

Here are some words to get you started:

Red _____

Day _____

Pot _____

_____

_____

_____

_____

_____

_____

_____

ANSWERS

P8
A = ROCKY, **B** = RUBBLE,
C = MARSHALL,
D = CHASE, **E** = SKYE,
F = ZUMA

P9
The missing pup is Marshall.

P11
FIRE! COME QUICK!

P12

P13 Path B.

P15

P17 Rocky doesn't have a match.

P18

P19

1. Rubble, **2.** Rocky, **3.** Skye,
4. Marshall

PAGES 22-23 **1.** C, **2.** B, **3.** A, **4.** B

P25

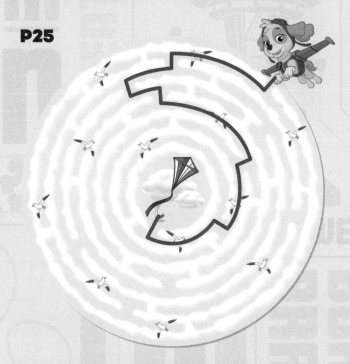

Skye meets 4 birds on her way.

PAGES 26-27
1. 3 lambs, **2.** Rubble,
3. 10 carrots, **4.** Pumpkins,
5. Ladybird.

P29
There are 12 fish in total.

P33

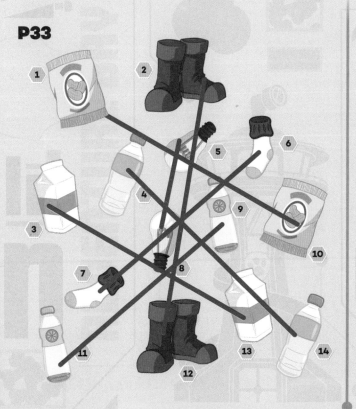

P39
Tracker met 3 skunks.
Tracker found Carlos
A snake is hiding in the jungle.

P40

P42
1. Skye, **2.** Zuma, **3.** Rocky,
4. Ryder, **5.** Tracker

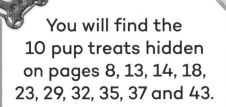

You will find the
10 pup treats hidden
on pages 8, 13, 14, 18,
23, 29, 32, 35, 37 and 43.